SUSSEX WATER

FRANK GREGORY and RON MARTIN

S. B. Publications

First published in 1997 by S.B. Publications
c/o 19 Grove Road, Seaford, East Sussex BN25 1TP

ISBN 1 85770 134 8

Typeset by JEM Lewes;
printed and bound by MFP Design and Print,
Longford Trading Estate, Thomas Street,
Stretford, Manchester M32 0JT.

Front and Back Cover: Lurgashall Mill
Title Page: Albourne Mill wheel

CONTENTS

Bailey's Mill, Coolham, see page 101

PREFACE

ENQUIRE anywhere in Sussex for information on watermills and windmills and the advice will be – 'you want to contact Frank Gregory about that'.

Frank has been studying mills since the 1930s and is a recognised authority not only in Sussex but at national and international levels, and he is active in the windmill and watermill section of The Society for the Preservation of Ancient Buildings.

In 1968, when The Sussex Industrial Archaeology Study Group was set up, Frank was appropriately the co-ordinator of the survey of natural power sites. In 1973 the title of this organisation was changed to The Sussex Industrial Archaeology Society and in 1988 an associated Sussex Mills Group was formed.

Through all these changes Frank has played a prominent part and is still a vital contributor through his position on the committees of the society and the mills group. At an early stage he contributed, to the society's survey of Sussex industrial monuments, the vast amount of information that he had already collected on mills, including a superb series of drawings of watermills that he had made mainly in the 1930s.

The society has long been of the opinion that these deserve a wider audience, and our thanks are extended to Steve Benz of SB Publications for making this book possible.

Other members of The Sussex Industrial Archaeology Society have also provided material for a publication that will stand as a tribute to Frank's pioneering endeavours. They are Ron Martin, secretary of the society, who wrote the captions and contributed drawings of the operation of watermills; Tony Yeoward, who provided glossary definitions; Martin Brunnarius, author of The Windmills of Sussex (Phillimore 1979), who wrote the foreword; Don Cox, secretary of the Sussex Mills Group, who advised

on the text.

This book contains most of the sketches made by Frank Gregory but space has precluded the inclusion of all. Those omitted are held by the society and may be seen by contacting the secretary, Ron Martin, on 01273 271330. Further information about The Sussex Industrial Archaeology Society, the Sussex Mills Group and the society's journal, *Sussex Industrial History,* and other publications is also available from the secretary.

Brian Austen
Editor
The Sussex Industrial Archaeology Society

The wheel of Newbridge Mill, Hartfield

FOREWORD

THIS presentation of Frank Gregory's watermill sketches is a tribute to one who has been dedicated to the well being of Sussex mills for more than 60 years. It is fitting that The Sussex Industrial Archaeology Society should sponsor the work. Frank has been a stalwart in his support of all aspects of the society's activities, and gives advice and practical assistance to all who ask. He is a truly committed industrial archaeologist. In fact, Frank is linked with the history of the London Brighton and South Coast Railway - his grandfather Gregory being the driver whose quick reaction during the Clayton Tunnel disaster in 1861 saved many lives. Frank's father also worked at the Brighton locomotive works during William Stoudley's time.

From early beginnings in the 1930s Frank explored the more local mills on his push bike, making sketches and completing them at home. At weekends the Gregory family visited the more distant highways and byways of Sussex by car and young Frank always took along sketching equipment. In his teens Frank was very much aware of the contemporary writings of Thurston Hopkins and Ernest Straker, and of the survey work of Hemming and H E S Simmons. During breaks from college he cycled around the county exploring wood and vale, and sketching mills to be penned in later at home.

At the time Frank was a member of The Brighton and Hove Archaeological Society and was involved in excavations at Mount Caburn, Plumpton Plain and Whitehawk Camp. His interest and involvement was such that he went on to become president of the society.

During the period of Frank's watermill survey many were still turning and earning an honest living, but those mills that had become idle were being allowed to decay. Frank kept records of the state of each mill and helped wherever possible by encouraging and involving himself in restoration work. He was a

regular visitor to many mills while they were still working, and knew the millers personally.

In all, Frank recorded and drew more than 100 Sussex watermills before the Second World War and in this way has kept them alive. Many are now gone, or have been extensively converted for alternative use. Others are very much more intact and can still operate when the penstock is opened, allowing the wheel to start gently turning once more.

Martin Brunnarius

Hardham Mill

INTRODUCTION

THE watermill, for many years a familiar part of the Sussex scene, has a history which dates back to Roman times. The first references occurred in the Greek part of the Roman Empire in the first century BC. This type of mill, described by Vitruvius, consisted of a waterwheel on a horizontal shaft, geared to a vertical spindle driving an upper pair of millstones. Such an arrangement is the basis for all subsequent mill gearing. The watermill was in active use in Sussex in Saxon times and the Domesday Book records 150-160 in the county.

In the conventional mill the type of waterwheel - overshot, breast or undershot - was determined by the head and amount of water available. The overshot wheel is found on the headwaters of a stream, where there is considerable fall but a limited water supply, and the wheel is driven by the weight of the water. In mid courses the breast wheel was used and in lower courses the undershot wheel with radial floats was used, driven by slight fall but larger volume of water.

Industrial wheels of the 19th century are often backshot, or high breast, where water was brought almost to the top of the wheel, which turned it backwards, thereby giving the power of an overshot wheel, but preventing uneven running due to surging of the water.

Most mills were corn mills, but water power in the past was also very important to the iron industry of the Sussex Weald. From the 15th to the early 19th centuries furnace and hammer ponds provided power for blowing the blast furnaces and forging the resulting iron. The last of these to work was Ashburnham Furnace, where a wheel pit is still to be seen. A hammer and anvil from Boarzell Forge at Etchingham are displayed at the Anne of Cleves House museum in Lewes. A sawmill powered by an iron overshot wheel made by Neve of Heathfield still stands at the estate workshop in Brightling Park, although it is now in a derelict state. Small wheels used to pump water are also found on various large estates.

The usual drive in a watermill consists of a pitwheel on the end of the waterwheel shaft in the mill. This meshes with a wallower fixed on an upright shaft. Above it is set a great spur wheel and small pinions (stone nuts) which mesh with this to convey the drive to the millstones. One, two, three or four pairs of stones are on the floor above. In the majority of mills the upright shaft is continued to the ceiling of the stone floor and from a crown wheel various lay shafts power auxiliary machinery.

When the mill is in use the corn is drawn to the top by means of the sack hoist and tipped in to corn bins on the top, or bin, floor. It then descends by gravity to the stone floor below, where it enters the hopper above the millstones. From the hopper the grain falls into a sloping chute or 'shoe' leading to the 'eye' or hole in the centre of the stones. The slope of the shoe is not enough for grain to flow on its own; the shoe must be shaken. This is done by holding one side of the shoe by a spring against the three ribs on a spindle fixed in the centre of the eye. According to the speed of the stones, more or less corn is shaken into the eye of the stones. In use the mill is relatively silent except for the chatter of this spindle, and so it is always known as the 'miller's damsel'.

Of the millstones, the lower of each pair, the bedstone, is fixed. Only the top stone, the runner, turns, and the furrows cut into the facing surfaces lead the grain from the eye. By the time it reaches the edge of the stones the grain has been reduced to meal. As it emerges the meal is contained in the wooden casing surrounding the stones, and is carried around to where the wooden spout allows it to fall down into bins or sacks on the floor below.

IT was a privilege to have known these Sussex mills in the 1930s when a number were still at work, and before the present surge of house conversions. The last mills in commercial use using waterwheels to turn millstones shut down in the period 1960 to 1976. I well remember being at Cobbs Mill, Hurstpierpoint, in January 1996 when the last grain passed from the hopper to the millstones under the expert hands of Percy Trower who, with Fred Sayers, worked the mill - using a Tangye gas engine when the water was low. The last corn mill in use was Deans Mill at Lindfield, where the Polish miller Bernard Lynwood produced wholemeal flour until his retirement in 1976.

However, more recently, several mills have been restored to working order. Once of the earliest was Woods Mill at Small Dole, headquarters of The Sussex Wildlife Trust. The mill at Michelham Priory has been re-equipped with a single pair of millstones and a waterwheel in place of the turbine shown in my sketch. Until his death in 1995 veteran miller Gilbert Catt of Hailsham coaxed it to produce wholemeal flour for visitors. It still continues to operate with volunteer millers.

Park Mill at Batemans, Burwash, abandoned by Rudyard Kipling when he lived there, has been restored to working order for The National Trust, largely by volunteers from The Sussex Industrial Archaeology Society, and it too produces wholemeal flour for visitors. Another veteran, Sydney Ashdown, who ran Cross in Hand Windmill all his working life, operated Park Mill after his retirement.

Burton Mill, Barlavington, is also back in production again, but using a turbine, and Lurgashall Mill has been rebuilt at the Weald and Downs Open Air Museum at Singleton, and is in daily use grinding flour for visitors. More recently Bartley Mill at Wadhurst, using its old waterwheel, but with a rebuilt cog pit, is now busy again.

Apart from the mills that are open to the public, others that survive are private property and may be visited only by permission of the owners.

Frank Gregory

❑ The sketches that follow are in alphabetical order, by name of mill; each has a map reference and the date on which it was sketched.

ALDINGBOURNE MILL
(Aldingbourne SU 924046)

A small corn mill on Aldingbourne Rife, with all iron machinery. The overshot wheel was made by Morleys of Crawley and it drove three pairs of stones. The building was of flint rubble with brick dressings and had a gabled roof. It last worked in 1914 and was converted to domestic use in the 1950s, but retains most machinery. 15.9.51

BALCOMBE MILL
(Balcombe TQ 317304)

A medium sized corn mill on Shell Brook with a composite overshot wheel and iron penstock, all manufactured by Morleys of Crawley, and having four pairs of stones. The building had a brick lower storey and weatherboarded timber superstructure with a slated gabled roof. By 1957 all machinery had been removed. The crown wheel and stone cases were taken to Ifield Mill. The site is now partly beneath the Ardingly Reservoir and the mill has been converted into a house. 11.8.36

BARCOMBE MILLS (Barcombe TQ 432148)

A large corn and button mill on the River Ouse with wheels replaced by turbines. The building had a brick substructure and timber framed and ornate weatherboarded superstructure, with a half hipped roof covered with slate. There had been a mill on this site since Domesday, originally a corn mill with two pairs of stones. Subsequently it was converted to turbines and used to make buttons from vegetable ivory until it was burnt down in 1939. 16.2.36

BARTLEY MILL, FRANT (Wadhurst TQ 632355)

A medium sized corn mill with an iron overshot wheel manufactured by S Medhurst of Lewes in 1877, with iron shaft. The building is of brick with weatherboarded gable and a gabled roof covered with clay tiles. The mill was working until the 1930s and it was derelict in 1937. The machinery and hursting were rebuilt c 1986 and the mill is now restored to working order. 10.5.37

BEX MILL (Heyshott SU 884187)

A medium sized corn will with cast iron overshot wheel driving three pairs of stones, through an iron pit wheel, wallower and spur wheel. The building is of brick with half hipped roof covered with slates. The mill was working until the 1960s and was converted into a house in the late 1970s. The machinery was removed but the wheel and pit wheel remain. 10.4.36

BIGNOR MILL (Bignor SU 982148)

A medium sized corn mill with iron overshot wheel, wooden upright shaft and spur wheel. The building is of brick, partly rendered and with slate covered gabled roof. It has been converted to domestic use and all machinery has been removed, but there is now a smaller wooden waterwheel. 25.7.36

BIRCHEN BRIDGE MILL,
Mannings Heath (Nuthurst TQ 193291)

Two mills side by side, the east one a timber framed structure with a wooden overshot wheel driving millstones and a lathe via a layshaft. The west mill, brick built, had a cast iron waterwheel with a penstock by W Cooper, dated 1865. It was used latterly for pumping water (1936) and driving a dynamo. A turbine, never installed, lay outside the walls (see bottom left of drawing). All was demolished in 1959. 25.3.37

BOLEBROKE MILL
(Hartfield TQ 481373)

A small corn mill with wooden overshot wheel and shaft driving two pairs of stones through iron machinery. The building has a brick substructure and timber framed and weatherboarded superstructure with a gabled roof with lucam covered with clay tiles. The mill was working in 1937 driving a chaff cutter and has now been converted into a house, but with the machinery intact. 11.4.37

BOLNEY MILL
(Bolney TQ 261217)

A small corn mill with iron overshot wheel manufactured by S Medhurst & Son of Lewes in 1861, and an iron shaft driving two pairs of stones through all iron machinery and penstock by JW Holloway of Shoreham. The building was of brick or stone construction with gabled gambrel roof covered with clay tiles. The mill was demolished in 1964 but the penstock remains. 3.1.36

BORINGWHEEL MILL,
Cacklestreet (Maresfield TQ 457264)

A small corn mill with composite overshot wheel and iron shaft driving two pairs of stones through an iron pit wheel, wallower, crown and spur wheel with wooden upright shaft. The building has a brick substructure and a timber framed and weatherboarded superstructure with a half hipped roof covered with clay tiles. The mill was derelict in 1936, without stones, and has now been partially restored. 22.3.36.

BOSHAM MILL (Bosham SU 803038)

A medium sized corn mill on Bosham Stream which had three overshot wheels, two internal iron wheels with wooden shafts and one external wooden wheel with wooden shaft. The brick, timber framed and weatherboarded building was disused in 1936. The superstructure was demolished in 1954 and rebuilt to form a yacht club headquarters. Mills on the site were recorded in the Domesday Book. 5.7.36

BRAMBLETYE MILL (Forest Row TQ 416353)

A medium sized corn mill with wooden wheel with iron shaft driving three pairs of stones through iron machinery. The building had a brick substructure and a timber framed and weatherboarded superstructure with a gambrel roof covered with slate. The mill ceased working in 1937 and was burnt down c 1958. 15.8.36

BREWHURST MILL
(Loxwood TQ 045310)

A medium sized corn mill with one internal iron overshot wheel and one iron low breast shot external flood wheel manufactured by King of Rudgwick with wooden shaft and with a complete set of iron machinery. The building has a sandstone rubble substructure and a timber framed and weatherboarded superstructure. The hipped roof is slate covered. The mill was burnt out in the 19th century and rebuilt with an additional storey. It ceased operating by water power in 1933 when a diesel engine was installed. It is currently awaiting restoration. 10.5.36

BROADBRIDGE MILL (Broadbridge Heath TQ 144304)

A large corn mill on the River Arun with one wheel replaced by a turbine. The building had a brick substructure and timber framed and weatherboarded superstructure with a gabled roof covered with corrugated iron. It was derelict in 1936 and demolished in about 1960. There are no visible remains. 4.8.36

BUGSELL MILL (Hurst Green TQ 723255)

A small corn mill on the River Rother with two overshot wheels, one iron external one with wooden shaft, and one internal one. The building has a brick substructure and timber framed, weatherboarded superstructure, with a gabled roof. It was derelict c 1950 and has since been demolished.

BURTON MILL (Barlavington SU 978180)

A medium sized corn and saw mill on Burton Mill Pond, with two overshot clasp arm wooden wheels, replaced by turbines (one in 1929) which were used to drive woodworking machinery. The building is of sandstone rubble with brick dressings and has a half hipped roof covered with clay tiles. It was fully restored in the 1980s, for corn grinding, and is still working. 10.4.36

BUXTED MILL (Buxted TQ 495233)

A medium sized corn mill on the River Uck with iron overshot wheel and shaft driving three pairs of stones through an iron pit wheel, wallower and upright shaft. The mill was working in 1936 but by 1959 all the internal machinery had been removed and the building had been converted into a house. The wheel remains. 30.7.36

CHANTRY MILL, Storrington (Sullington TQ 092138)

A small corn mill formerly with overshot wheel replaced by a turbine with hursting and boiler which were extant in 1936. The building is part flint with brick quoins and dressings, and part timber framed and weatherboarded under a half hipped roof. The mill was derelict in 1936 and converted into a house in the 1960s, by which date all the machinery was removed. 30.5 36

COBB'S MILL (Hurstpierpoint TQ 274189)

A large corn mill with iron overshot wheel driving four pairs of stones through an iron pit wheel, spur wheel and lay shaft. There is a Tangye gas auxiliary engine with gas producer plant. The building has a brick substructure and timber framed and weather-boarded superstructure with gabled roof covered with clay tiles. The mill was probably rebuilt in 1869 and was working until 1966. All machinery is intact but the wheel has lost its buckets. 19.1.36

COCKING MILL
(Cocking SU 880176)

A small corn mill on Coster's Brook with iron overshot wheel and pit wheel. The building is of squared rubble sandstone with brick quoins with the half hipped roof covered with clay tiles. It was derelict in 1941 and converted into a house c 1960. No machinery remains. 25.3.41

COSTER'S MILL (West Lavington SU 895206)

A medium sized corn mill with overshot iron wheel manufactured by Chorley's Foundry at Cocking, with wooden shaft, iron pit wheel and wallower and wooden upright shaft. The building is of sandstone rubble with brick quoins and dressings and it has a clay tiled half hipped roof. The mill was built in 1835 and was converted into a house c 1970. The wheel was removed to Lurgashall Mill. 10.4.36

COURT MILL

(Steyning TQ 172105)

A small corn mill with iron overshot wheel with wooden shaft driving three pairs of stones through an iron pit wheel, wallower, upright shaft and spur wheel. The building has a brick substructure and part brick, part timber framed and weatherboarded superstructure under a clay tiled, half hipped gambrel roof. There is an adjacent former corn store and a bakery at the rear. The mill had been working until about 1926 and was converted into a house in the 1930s. The bakery was once used to produce dog biscuits. Some machinery remains on the ground floor and the wheel is in a poor state. 11.1.36

DEAN'S MILL (Lindfield TQ 353261)

A large corn mill with iron breast shot wheel and shaft on the River Ouse, driving four pairs of stones through all iron machinery and with a complete set of auxiliary machinery. The building has a brick substructure and a timber framed and weatherboarded superstructure, and the gabled roof is clay tiled. The mill was rebuilt in its present form in 1881 after a storm. It was operated by the Horsfield family in 1936 and subsequently by a health food firm until 1976. It has been preserved in near working order. 9.2.36

DUNCTON MILL (Duncton SU 964166)

A medium sized corn mill with iron overshot wheel, wooden stone hurst, upright shaft and crown wheel driving three pairs of stones. The building is of sandstone rubble with brick quoins and a gabled roof. In 1936 the wheel was used for spraying the adjoining orchard. The mill is now derelict although it contains some machinery and is cared for as part of a fish farm. 16.8.36

DUNNING'S MILL (East Grinstead TQ 391368)

A medium sized corn mill with wooden overshot wheel with iron shaft and two pairs of stones. It was converted into a house in 1938 with the machinery intact, but this was removed by 1950. It became a public house in the 1960s and is now incorporated into a pub and sports complex. 3.4.38

DUNSTER'S MILL (Ticehurst TQ 689323)

A medium sized corn mill on the River Bewl with cast iron overshot wheel with wooden shaft driving at least three pairs of stones with iron pit wheel and lay shaft. The mill was complete in 1938 and was demolished in 1951 after a fire. The site is now beneath the Bewl Water reservoir, but some salvaged machinery was moved to the grounds of the re-erected Dunster's Mill House.

EBERNOE MILL
(Wassell Mill, Ebernoe SU 901280)

A small corn mill with iron overshot wheel. The building has brick substructure and timber framed and weatherboarded superstructure, with a gabled roof covered with clay tiles. The mill was complete but unused in 1936, the wheel having been reduced to half width and used to generate electricity. The building was converted into a house in the 1950s. The half width wheel is still in position but there is no machinery except the pit wheel. 28.6.36

FEN PLACE MILL (East Grinstead TQ 361366)

A small corn mill on the River Medway with brick substructure and timber framed and weatherboarded superstructure, and with a half hipped roof covered with clay tiles. The mill was derelict in 1936 and it has since been converted into a house. No machinery remains. 24.5.36

FITTLEWORTH MILL (Fittleworth TQ 008183)

A medium sized corn mill on the Western River Rother with two undershot clasp arm wooden wheels with iron shafts, one iron pit wheel and re-used wooden upright shaft. All other machinery is missing. The building is of Pulborough stone with brick quoins and dressings. It was derelict in 1937 and converted into a house in 1980. 18.4.57

FLETCHING MILL (Fletching TQ 423228)

A medium sized corn mill on the River Ouse with breast shot iron wheel by S Medhurst, and a shaft driving three pairs of stones through cast iron pit wheel and wooden upright shaft. The building was of brick with a gabled roof and tower with a lucam. It was working until 1939 and demolished in 1951. The square tower was used to view the Earl of Sheffield's cricket matches in Sheffield Park. 26.12.35

FRESHFIELD MILL
(Lindfield TQ 385244)

A small corn mill with iron undershot wheel. The building had a brick substructure with a timber framed and weatherboarded superstructure. The gabled roof was slate covered. The mill was derelict in 1936 and was demolished in the 1950s. 23.2.36

GIBBON'S MILL (Rudgwick TQ 071308)

A medium sized corn mill on the River Arun with, formerly, an undershot wheel driving two pairs of stones. The original machinery had a wooden crown wheel. The building has a brick substructure and part brick, part timber framed and weatherboarded superstructure with a gabled roof. The original mill was extended in 1860 by William Botting. The wheel was replaced by a turbine in 1898 for electric generation. There is now no machinery and the mill has been converted into a house. 10.5.36

HAMMOND'S MILL (Clayton TQ 300176)

A large corn mill also used for wire drawing with iron overshot wheel and shaft manufactured by Coopers of Henfield in 1870, with all iron machinery comprising pit wheel, wallower, upright shaft and spur wheel. The building had a brick substructure and timber framed and weatherboarded superstructure with a half hipped roof covered with clay tiles. The mill was extended in 1880, derelict in 1936 and demolished in 1975. Some of the machinery has been re-used at Ifield Mill. 5.1.36

HAYWARDS HEATH MILL (Bridger's Mill, Haywards Heath TQ 329249)

A large corn mill with iron overshot wheel with wooden shaft and iron penstock cast in the Regent Iron Foundry in Brighton in 1843. The mill was built in 1840 and was worked intermittently until 1920, aided by a Hornsby gas engine with its own producer gas plant, which was converted to town gas in 1921. The engine ran until 1944, after which the mill was electrically powered. The wheel, long gone, was about 28ft in diameter. The mill was demolished in 1969. The site has now been redeveloped.

HAZELWICK MILL (Crawley TQ 287379)

A medium sized corn mill on Gatwick Stream with two overshot wheels, one iron with an iron shaft. The building had a brick substructure with timber framed superstructure covered with weatherboarding and a gabled roof and lucam covered with clay tiles. The mill was complete but disused in 1936 but has since been demolished. The site has been completely altered by the building of Crawley new town. 24.5.36

HELLINGLY MILL (Hellingly TQ 585125)

A small corn mill with iron overshot wheel and shaft by Upfield & Sons of Catsfield, driving three pairs of stones through iron machinery. The building has a brick substructure and a timber framed and weatherboarded superstructure with a half hipped roof. The mill was being used as a tea house in 1936 and has recently been restored to working order with a new iron wheel made by the British Engineerium. 26.7.36

HEMPSTEAD MILL (Uckfield TQ 483217)

A large corn mill on the River Uck with breast shot wheel. The brick, timber framed and weatherboarded building has a half hipped roof, and lucam covered with slates. The mill was operating in 1936 and has recently been used to generate electricity. Most of the machinery is extant. The building is now used as a workshop. 9.4.36

HIGH HURSTWOOD MILL (Buxted TQ 493261)

A small corn mill with iron overshot wheel and shaft manufactured by S Medhurst & Son in 1867, driving two pairs of stones through iron pit wheel and wallower, and wooden upright shaft spur wheel and crown wheel. The building has a brick substructure and timber framed and weatherboarded superstructure with half hipped roof covered with clay tiles. The mill was derelict in 1936 but is still cared for by its owner. 30.7.36

HIGHBRIDGE MILL
(Cuckfield TQ 297236)

A small corn mill with iron overshot wheel and shaft driving two pairs of stones through an iron pit wheel, wooden upright shaft, wallower and clasp arm spur wheel and iron spur wheel. The building is of brick with weatherboarded gable and a clay tiled roof. It was disused in 1936. The upper part has been converted into a house but the machinery is still intact. 26.1.36

HORSEBRIDGE MILL (Hailsham TQ 581113)

A large commercial corn mill with one iron low breast shot wheel and one turbine driving six pairs of stones. The building is of brick with a gabled roof. The mill was owned by McDougalls from 1921 to 1969. The mill machinery was replaced by electrically driven roller mills with water being used occasionally until the 1940s. Since then all the internal machinery has been removed with only the wheel extant. 13.12.36

HORSTED KEYNES MILL (Horsted Keynes TQ 380286)

A small corn mill with wooden overshot wheel driving two pairs of stones, with iron pit wheel, upright shaft, spur wheel and wallower. The building has a brick substructure with timber framed and weatherboarded superstructure, and has a gabled roof of clay tiles. The mill was in use intermittently in 1936 for grinding and for powering a saw bench, but fell into disuse after the Second World War. The mill is now being reconstructed. The wooden overshot wheel has been rebuilt by the present owner and can now generate electricity. 29.3.36

HUGGETT'S FURNACE MILL (Hadlow Down TQ 534259)

A small corn mill with iron overshot wheel with wooden shaft and iron pit wheel. The building has a brick substructure with a timber boarded and weatherboarded superstructure with a half hipped roof covered with clay tiles. The mill has not worked since the 1900s. The machinery was removed in the 1940s. It has since been converted into a house. 11.10.36

HURST MILL, South Harting (Harting SU 765210)

A small corn mill with wooden overshot wheel and shaft. The building is of brick with half hipped roof covered with Horsham stone slabs. By 1944 it had been adapted for generating electricity and for pumping. The wheel was rebuilt in the 1940s with iron hub and radial wooden spokes. No milling machinery remains. 20.6.44

IFIELD MILL
(Crawley TQ 245364)

A large corn mill on Ifield Brook, with iron overshot wheel and shaft and high pen trough. The building has a brick substructure and timber framed weatherboarded superstructure with a gabled roof, and a lucam covered with clay tiles. This mill is on an old ironworking site and was originally built in 1683. By 1959 there was no internal machinery. It is now being restored by The Sussex Industrial Archaeology Society using material from Hammond's Mill. The restored waterwheel now turns and a new spur wheel has been constructed.
11.8.36

ISFIELD MILL (Isfield TQ 448181)

A large commercial corn mill with turbine on the River Uck which drove several pairs of stones. The building is brick with a gabled roof covered with slate. By the 1950s three pairs of stones were being driven by an Armfield turbine and until recently the modern equipment was operated by electricity. It has been sold for conversion. 14.4.36

LEIGH MILL, Goddards Green (Hurstpierpoint TQ 287211)

A small corn mill with iron overshot wheel and penstock manufactured by Coopers, driving two pairs of stones through an iron pit wheel, wallower and crown wheel, and with a wooden upright shaft. The building had a brick substructure with timber framed and weatherboarded superstructure, and a clay tiled gambrel roof. It was derelict in 1936 and demolished in the 1950s. The stones are now at Jill Windmill, Clayton. 2.1.36

LOD'S BRIDGE MILL (Lodsworth SU 933210)

A medium sized corn mill on the Western River Rother with two undershot wheels with wooden shafts. One drove a pair of stones through a one step gear, and was known locally as the 'Roman mill'. The other drove two pairs of stones through a conventional spur wheel. The mill was derelict in 1936 and was converted into a house c 1960 when the machinery was removed. 16.8.36

LOWER MILL, Cockhaise (Lindfield TQ 378257)

A small corn mill on Cockhaise Brook with iron overshot wheel manufactured by A Shaw of Lewes in 1883, with wooden shaft driving three pairs of stones with a wooden upright shaft. The building has a stone and brick substructure and timber framed and weatherboarded superstructure. The half hipped roof is clay tiled. There is a stone inscribed 'FRANCIS WYATT 1697' and a brick inscribed 'AH 1774'. The mill had all machinery except the upright shaft removed by 1936 and has since been converted into a house. Another adjacent mill known as Upper Mill was demolished before 1936. 23.2.36

LOWER MILL,
Nutbourne (Pulborough TQ 076186)

A small corn mill with overshot wheel, timber shaft and iron pit wheel. The buildings were of sandstone rubble with half hipped roof. The mill was derelict in 1936 and demolished in the late 1930s. 27.7.36

LURGASHALL MILL
(Lurgashall SU 940259)

A small corn mill which at one time had two overshot wheels running in tandem with wooden shafts, iron pitwheel and wooden upright shaft with spur wheel. The remaining wheel was manufactured by Chorley of Cocking and was previously used at Coster's Mill, West Lavington. The building is of sandstone rubble, the gable cladding is weatherboarded and the roof is half hipped and covered with clay tiles. The mill was complete but unused in 1936, was almost washed away in 1963, and was taken down and re-erected in the Weald and Downland Open Air Museum at Singleton in the 1980s, where it is working. 28.6.36

MICHELHAM PRIORY MILL (Arlington TQ 557093)

A small corn mill on the River Cuckmere formerly with breast shot wheel replaced by a turbine driving four pairs of stones with sluices by Upfield & Sons of Catsfield, dated 1890, and by J Whittington & Sons of Brighton, dated 1928. The turbine, installed in the 1930s, was removed in 1959. The Sussex Archaeological Society has since restored the mill. A new iron waterwheel and machinery were installed in the summer of 1997. 17.5.36

MILLAND MILL
(Milland SU 836275)

A small corn mill with iron overshot wheel by the Weydon Iron Company of Guildford, with wooden shaft. The building is of coursed sandstone rubble and has a clay tiled gabled roof. The mill was converted into a house by 1937 with all the machinery removed except for the water wheel. 6.6.37

MOAT MILL
(Mayfield TQ 590249)

A small corn mill with iron overshot wheel and shaft manufactured by Neve Brothers, driving two pairs of stones through an iron pit wheel, spur wheel with the upright shaft, wallower and crown wheel all of wood. The building has brick substructure and timber framed and weatherboarded superstructure with a gabled roof. The mill was derelict in 1936 but with machinery complete, and it has since been converted into a house, with machinery remaining. 11.10.36

NEW MILL, Crowborough Warren (Withyham TQ 494320)

A large corn mill with iron overshot wheel, of more than 30ft diameter, and shaft driving at least three pairs of stones with lay shaft. The wheel was fed from a stone aqueduct. The building is of stone rubble with a half hipped roof covered with slates. The mill was derelict in 1937. In 1949 only the roofless walls remained and about twenty years later all the walls were demolished, only the spillway being extant. Flour for Queen Victoria's wedding cake is said to have been supplied by this mill. 1.8.37

NEWBRIDGE MILL, Colemans Hatch (Hartfield TQ 345328)

A small corn mill with iron overshot wheel and shaft driving three pairs of stones through iron pit wheel, upright shaft, wallower and spur wheel with a lay shaft from the crown wheel. The building has a sandstone substructure and timber framed and weatherboarded superstructure with a gabled roof covered with clay tiles. The mill was mostly complete in 1936 and had a partial house conversion by the 1960s. The machinery was stripped out in 1985 and a glass fibre wheel was installed to drive an electric generator. 14.6.36

NORTH MILL
(Easebourne SU 889220)

A large corn mill on the Western River Rother with two low breast shot wheels, one wooden with a wooden shaft and one iron with an iron shaft, driving two pairs of stones through an iron pit wheel, wallower and upright shaft. The building is of sandstone rubble with a gabled roof. The mill was in use in 1936, subsequently it became a warehouse and has now been converted into a house. No machinery remains, but one of the waterwheels is preserved in Haxted Mill Museum, Surrey 14.6.36

NORTHBROOK MILL, West Ashling (Funtington SU 808077)

A medium sized corn mill with iron overshot wheel and shaft manufactured by M and WT Sett of Godalming. There was a large cast iron penstock and the mill originally had four pairs of stones. The building is of brick with a half hipped roof covered with clay tiles. There is a date stone of 1721. The mill was used for paper making c 1830. It has now been completely demolished. 2.6.53

OLD MILL, Nutbourne (Pulborough TQ 076187)

A small corn mill with overshot wheel. The building is of sandstone rubble with brick quoins and dressings, the gable is weatherboarded and the roof is clay tiled. The mill was empty in 1936 and the building has now been converted into a house. 5.4.36

OLD PLACE MILL
(Pulborough TQ 044190)

A small mill with wooden overshot clasp arm wheel and shaft. The buildings are of sandstone rubble with half hipped, clay tiled roof. The mill machinery was removed in 1936 and the building was converted into a house, with additions on the north side. 27.7.36

PARK MILL

Batemans (Burwash TQ 670233)

A small corn mill on the River Dudwell with wooden overshot wheel and shaft driving three pairs of stones through iron pit wheel and wallower and wooden upright shaft, spur wheel and formerly a crown wheel. The building has a brick substructure and timber framed and weatherboarded superstructure with a half hipped roof covered with clay tiles. The mill was probably built in 1795. Rudyard Kipling installed a Gilkes turbine which drove a Crompton generator. It ceased to grind corn in 1902 and both the mill and generator were fully restored between 1970 and 1975. Today, a pair of peak stones driven by a cast iron stone nut off the spur wheel produce wholemeal flour. Formerly two pairs of burr stones were driven by wooden stone nuts with detachable cogs. 31.5.36

PLUMPTON MILL (Plumpton TQ 362150)

A medium sized corn mill with overshot iron wheel manufactured by A Shaw of Lewes in 1892, driving two pairs of stones through an iron pit wheel and vertical shaft. The mill was used in 1932 for electricity generation and pumping, and in 1961 to drive a saw bench. In about 1980 the mill was restored and reconstructed to drive one pair of stones. 28.1.36

PLUMPTON PLACE MILL (Plumpton TQ 361136)

A medium sized corn mill with overshot wheel. The building has brick substructure and timber framed and weatherboarded superstructure with gabled roof covered with clay tiles. The mill was converted into a house in the 1930s and the wheel replaced recently. 28.1.36

PLUMPTON UPPER MILL (Plumpton TQ 362147)

A very small corn mill with iron overshot wheel by A Shaw of Lewes, dated 1886, iron shaft, pit wheel, upright shaft, wallower, spur wheel and lay shaft. The building is of brick with a gambrel roof covered with clay tiles. The mill was derelict in 1935 and is currently being restored. 27.12.35

POLEGATE MILL
(Polegate TQ 579040)

A medium sized mill with iron overshot wheel and shaft driving three pairs of stones through an iron pit wheel, wallower and spur wheel and wooden upright shaft. The building was part brick and part flint rubble with brick quoins and dressings, with half hipped gabled roof. The mill was working up to the 1950s but the pond was drained in 1959 and it has since been demolished and a housing estate occupies the site. The wheel, now rebuilt, is at Wateringbury Mill in Kent. 17.6.36

POUNSLEY MILL
(Hadlow Down TQ 52819)

A very small corn mill on Tickerage Stream with overshot wheel. The building has a brick substructure and timber framed and weather-boarded superstructure with a gabled roof. The mill had all the machinery removed by 1936. It now stands in the middle of a field, having lost its water supply. 12.4.36

POYNINGS MILL
(Poynings TQ 260123)

A small corn mill with wooden overshot wheel with iron shaft, pit wheel and spur wheel. The building had a brick substructure and timber framed and weatherboarded superstructure, with clay tiled gambrel roof. The mill was derelict in 1936 and has since been demolished. 1.2.36

RACKHAM MILL (Parham TQ 046141)

A small corn mill with iron overshot wheel and shaft, iron pit wheel, wallower and spur wheel and wooden upright shaft and crown wheel. The building is of flint rubble with brick quoins and dressings, and it has a half hipped roof covered with corrugated iron., The mill was complete but unused in 1936 and remains the same. 8.11.36

RATHAM MILL, West Ashling (Funtington SU 811063)

A medium sized corn mill with iron overshot wheel, penstock manufactured by Chorley's of Midhurst, cast iron pit wheel, spur wheel and wallower and pitch pine upright shaft. The building is of brick with a half hipped roof covered with slates. A turbine was installed for electricity generation in 1936. The mill was power operated but the sack hoist still used the water power. All the machinery and the turbine remain but the mill is not in working order. It became redundant when a large modern mill was built alongside, but this has also ceased working. The owner hopes to save the old mill. 8.11.36

ROWFANT MILL (Worth TQ 315377)

A medium sized corn mill with iron overshot wheel and penstock (dated 1869) manufactured by J Morley of Crawley. The shaft extended outwards to an auxiliary belt drive. The building has a brick substructure and timber framed and weatherboarded superstructure with a gambrel roof clad in clay tiles. The mill was derelict in 1936 and was converted into a house in 1946. 6.12.36

ROWNER MILL Rowner Farm (Billingshurst TQ 071260)
A medium sized corn mill on the River Arun with low breast shot wooden clasp arm wheel and shaft, iron pit wheel and wallower, wooden upright shaft and ornate spur wheel. Adjoining was a corn mill adapted for water pumping with an iron undershot wheel. The site was derelict in 1936 and the mill was demolished in 1966. 9.7.36

RUCKFORD MILL
Hurstpierpoint TQ 293149)

A large corn mill with two overshot wheels with wooden shafts, one iron and one wooden, driving three pairs of stones. It has all iron penstocks by W Cooper (dated 1876 and 1879), pit wheels, upright shafts, spur wheels and crown wheel (except one in wood). There was a complete set of machinery, including a centrifugal governor and an auxiliary oil engine in 1936. The original mill was built in 1738. It was converted into a house in the 1960s, but still retaining its machinery.
19.1.36

SHEFFIELD FARM MILL (Fletching TQ 415257)

A small corn mill on Annwood Brook with iron overshot wheel and shaft by S Medhurst, 1869, driving two pairs of stones through iron pit wheel and wallower and wooden horizontal shaft with stones mounted on a hursting. There is a wire machine driven by more modern iron shafting. The building is of brick and sandstone, partly timber framed and weatherboarded. The mill was built on a furnace site and was derelict in 1936. It is still intact, and the waterwheel has been restored. 19.3.36

SHERMANBURY MILL
(Shermanbury TQ 212186)

A small corn mill on the River Adur with low breast shot wheel. The building had a brick substructure with timber framed and tile hung superstructure, and with a slated half hipped roof. The mill was complete but unused in 1936 and was demolished in the 1950s. 12.1.36

SHILLINGLEE PARK MILL (Plaistow SU 971308)

A small corn mill with a turbine. The building is of brick with a clay tiled half hipped roof. The mill was converted into a house in 1936. No internal machinery remains, but the turbine and feeder pipes are extant. 27.9.36

SHORTBRIDGE MILL (Fletching TQ 450213)

A medium sized corn mill on Shortbridge Stream with iron backshot wheel and shaft with iron machinery and an auxiliary steam engine. The building has a two storey brick bottom and is timber framed and weatherboarded above, with a gabled roof covered with slate. The mill was working in 1936 but shortly before the Second World War the internal machinery was removed. It was converted to a house c 1985. 14.4.36

SLAUGHAM PLACE FARM MILL (Slaugham TQ 258277)

A small corn mill on the River Ouse with overshot wheel replaced by a turbine. The building is of brick with a weatherboarded gable and a gambrel roof covered with clay tiles. The mill machinery was removed in 1937 and the building has since been used as a store. 31.3.37

SLIPPER MILL, Emsworth (Southbourne SU 753054)

A small corn tidemill with undershot timber clasp arm wheel and shaft and adjacent large granary. The building was of brick with a gabled roof covered with clay tiles. The wheel was extant in 1936 but the machinery was missing. It was demolished in the 1960s. The granary has been converted into four houses. The tidemill pond and gates still exist. 5.8.36

STONE MILL
(Rotherfield TQ 542264)

A small corn mill with wheel replaced by a turbine used for electricity generation. The building has a brick substructure and timber framed and weatherboarded superstructure with gabled roof. It has been converted into a house. 12.9.36.

STORRINGTON MILL
(Bine's or Gatley's Mill) (TQ 087144)

A small corn mill on the River Stor with iron overshot wheel driving one pair of stones. The penstock was manufactured by Black Aller of Steyning. Latterly it had an electrically driven hammer mill. The building was of brick, rendered on one face and with a half hipped roof covered with clay tiles. The mill was in use in 1936 and has since been demolished. The penstock and some of the internal machinery is now at Wateringbury Mill in Kent. 27.7.36

STREAM MILL (Chiddingly TQ 565154)

A small corn mill with iron overshot wheel with wooden shaft formerly driving two pairs of stones through iron pit wheel and horizontal shaft. The building has a brick substructure and a part brick and part timber framed and corrugated iron superstructure with gabled roof covered with corrugated iron. The internal machinery was removed in 1936 and the building was converted into a house c 1985. 2.3.36

TERWICK MILL (Trotton with Chithurst SU 830221)

Two adjacent corn mills on the Western River Rother. Old Mill was a small corn mill with iron breast shot wheel, driving one pair of stones with iron pit wheel and wallower. New Mill, of c 1740, was medium sized with iron breast shot wheel and shaft, driving two pairs of stones through an iron pit wheel and wallower, wooden upright shaft, spur wheel and crown wheel. This mill ceased operating in 1966. It has been converted into a house but retains basic machinery and two pairs of stones.

TICKERAGE MILL, Blackboys (Framfield TQ 515210)

A small corn mill with iron overshot wheel manufactured by S Medhurst & Son of Lewes in 1868 and wooden shaft driving two pairs of stones through iron machinery. The building had a brick substructure and timber framed and weatherboarded superstructure with a gabled and half hipped roof covered with clay tiles. The mill was derelict in 1936 and the machinery and wheel were removed by 1958. 30.7.36

TOWN MILL (Horsham TQ 168303)

A large commercial corn mill on the River Arun with two iron wheels, one overshot and one a breast shot flood wheel with Poncelet buckets, driving four pairs of stones. There were two iron pit wheels and a lay shaft and the mill had an auxiliary steam engine. The building was of brick with a gabled roof. It was rebuilt in 1867, used until the 1950s and converted into a house in the 1960s. 4.8.36

TOWN MILL and **UCKFIELD ROLLER MILL** (Uckfield TQ 473209)

Town Mill is a medium sized corn mill on the River Uck with iron overshot wheel and shaft. The building was timber framed covered partly with corrugated iron with half hipped roof covered with clay tiles. The adjacent Roller Mill was a large mill with turbines built in brick as an extension to Town Mill. The mills were working in 1936 and have since been converted into offices. 9.4.36

UPTON'S MILL
(Framfield TQ 504211)

A small corn mill with iron overshot wheel and shaft, driving three pairs of stones through a cast iron pit wheel, wallower and wooden upright shaft and spur wheel. The name of S Medhurst and date 1873 are cast on the penstock. The building has a brick substructure and timber framed and weatherboarded superstructure with half hipped roof with lucam covered with clay tiles. The mill was complete but unused in 1936 and was converted into a house in 1962, all machinery being removed except the upright shaft which has been re-used as a newel post.

VALEBRIDGE MILL (Holland's Mill, Cuckfield TQ 318212)

A small corn mill with iron overshot wheel and shaft, iron pit and spur wheel with wooden upright shaft. The building was of brick with a weatherboarded gable and clay tiled roof. It was derelict but complete in 1936 and burnt down around 1962. There are no remains on site. 26.1.36

WANFORD MILL (Rudgwick TQ 084326)

A medium sized corn mill on the River Arun with two iron breast shot wheels, one with iron shaft and one with wooden shaft driving two pairs of stones. The two storey building has a third storey extension, timber framed and weatherboarded and the clay tiled roof is gabled. The mill was derelict in 1937 and it has since been converted into a house. The remains of one wheel were extant in 1980. 26.7.37

WARNHAM MILL (Warnham TQ 168322)

A medium sized corn mill with iron overshot wheel driving three pairs of stones through iron pit wheel, wallower and crown wheel, and wooden upright shaft. The building has a sandstone rubble substructure with a brick superstructure and tile hung gable. The gabled roof is clad with Horsham slabs. The mill is complete and in running order, being partly used as an office. An adjacent pump house takes power from the wheel. 4.8.36

WEST ASHLING (Funtington SU 807073)

A large corn mill with breast shot wheel replaced by an Armfield turbine, and driving three pairs of stones. The building is of brick with hipped roof covered with slates, and it was surmounted by a hollow post mill by Armfield (demolished in 1955), driving three more pairs of stones. The mill was operational in 1936 and ceased working in 1941. It is now residential and the waterdriven machinery remains. 5.7.36

WOODS MILL, Small Dole (Henfield TQ 218137)

A medium sized corn mill with iron overshot wheel, pit wheel, wallower and crown wheel, and wooden vertical shaft. The iron penstock was manufactured by Neale and Cooper in 1854. There are two date stones, one inscribed T 1712 S and the other FB 1820. The mill was derelict in 1936 and during the Second World War the internal machinery was removed, except for the pit wheel which had a chain drive to an electricity generator. A hursting has since been reconstructed, with one pair of stones, and the mill is now the headquarters of The Sussex Wildlife Trust. 1.2.36

ADDITIONAL WATERMILLS

LIMITATIONS of space have prevented the inclusion of all the mill drawings produced by Frank Gregory. Additional drawings exist for a number of the mills that are illustrated in the book while other drawings and sketches exist for the following mills.

ALBOURNE MILL, Truslers Hill (Albourne TQ 249164)
A small corn mill on the Chess Brook, with wooden overshot wheel, pit wheel and wallower, and wooden spur wheel. The building had a brick substructure and weatherboarded timber superstructure with a half hipped roof. It was latterly worked by steam and was demolished in 1929. Sketch on title page.

BAILEY'S MILL, Coolham (Shipley TQ 1211234)
A small corn mill on the River Adur with wooden undershot wheel and shaft driving two pairs of stones. The building had a substructure of sandstone rubble with a brick superstructure and weatherboarded gable. The lucam was covered with sheet metal. The mill was empty of machinery in 1936 and demolished in the 1960s. There are now no visible remains. Sketch on Contents page.

BARNETT'S MILL (East Lavington SU 944195)
A medium sized corn mill. The building had a brick and stone substructure and timber framed and weatherboarded superstructure, with a half hipped roof covered with clay tiles. It was derelict, without machinery, c 1936 and has since been demolished.

BECKLEY FURNACE MILL (Beckley TQ 836211)
A small corn mill on the River Tillingham with iron overshot wheel. The building was of brick and was on the site of a former iron furnace. It had auxiliary steam power and was burnt down **c** 1909. Only the

lower walls are now standing with the wheel still extant.

BENHALL MILL (Frant TQ 607376)

A small corn mill with wooden overshot wheel and shaft driving three pairs of stones through a cast iron pit wheel and wooden upright shaft, spur wheel and crown wheel. The building was of brick. The mill was in ruins in 1938 and was demolished in the 1950s.

BIRDHAM TIDEMILL (Birdham SU 824011)

A medium sized corn mill at Birdham Pool with two undershot iron wheels with wooden buckets. The building has a brick substructure with tarred weatherboarding above, and a hipped roof covered with clay tiles. The mill was in use until the 1930s and is now used as a yacht clubhouse. All the machinery has been removed.

BISHOPSTONE TIDEMILLS (Seaford TQ 459002)

Very large tidemills with three wheels driving sixteen pairs of stones. The building was of brick and flint rubble, part rendered, with gabled roofs. The mills were demolished around the turn of the century. All that is now left are the culverts to three wheels.

BRIGHTLING BRICKWORKS, Oxleys Green (Brightling TQ 688223)

A small water powered pug mill with iron overshot wheel by Neves of Heathfield, probably cast from the same pattern as that at the Brightling Park Sawmill. The building has a brick lower storey and weatherboarded upper with tiled hipped roof. The brickwork remains but is in a derelict state.

BRIGHTLING PARK SAWMILL (Brightling TQ 684200)

A small corn and saw mill with iron overshot wheel and shaft, iron pit wheel and line shafting to operate a saw bench and other plant. The building is of brick with an M-shaped roof covered with clay tiles. The mill was originally built as an estate corn mill but was converted to a saw mill early in the 20th century. It was complete and working until after the Second World War but has since been allowed to become derelict.

BROADBRIDGE MILL (Bosham SU 8100534)

A corn mill on Bosham Stream. The original mill was burnt down. The remains of a later turbine were extant in 1961 and the site has now been redeveloped for housing.

BUCKSTEEP MILL (Warbleton TQ 653145)

A small corn mill on Christian's River with an iron overshot wheel and shaft with wooden upright shaft. The building is of squared sandstone rubble. There were the remains of the wheel and the lower storey in 1936.

Pug mill at Brightling Brickworks 17.4.38

BURY FARM MILL (Bury TQ 007150)

A corn mill, converted to pumping, with timber breast shot wheel with iron shaft. Only the wheel remains.

COX'S MILL (Burwash TQ 651201)

A small corn and saw mill on the Willingford Stream with former overshot wheel replaced by a turbine driving a saw bench and generator. The building is of stone with brick quoins, with a half hipped roof covered with clay tiles. The turbine had replaced the wheel by 1937 and was removed by 1956 to be replaced by a diesel engine. The building still stands but is without any machinery.

CROWSOLE MILL (Fittleworth TQ 005206)

A small corn mill with iron overshot wheel. The building is of sandstone rubble with a gabled roof covered with clay tiles. The mill machinery has been removed and the mill has been converted into a house.

CUT MILL (Bosham SU 799054)
A corn mill on Cutmill Creek with overshot wheel. It had become a house by 1937, with a rebuilt wheel.

DARWELL MILL (Brightling TQ 695198)
A small corn mill on the Darwell Stream with iron overshot wheel driving two pairs of stones through an iron pit wheel. The building was brick and had been demolished by 1936. Only the wheel, wheel pit and launder survived. Some foundations only are extant.

DURFORD MILL, Rogate (Harting SU 779232)
A medium sized corn mill with breast shot wheel replaced by a turbine driving two pairs of stones. The building is of brick with a half hipped roof. It was probably built in 1736 (or 1756) according to a date stone, and was last worked in 1919. It was derelict c 1938 and was incorporated in the 1950s into a large industrial building, since when it has had a variety of uses. No machinery exists.

FURNACE MILL, Cowden (Hartfield TQ 454399)
A medium sized corn mill on Kent Water with overshot wheel The building has a timber framed, weatherboarded superstructure with a tiled mansard roof. The mill became a house in the 1930s.

HALFWAY BRIDGE MILL (Lodsworth SU 930219)
A medium sized corn mill on the Western River Rother with breast shot wheel. The building is of brick with a gabled roof. There are two dated stones - HS 1872 and HB 1905. The mill had been converted into a factory by 1958 and was burnt out in the 1960s.

HARDHAM MILL (TQ 034178)
Impressive iron undershot waterwheels on the same shaft drove a roller mill plant in the mill building. The mill was out of use by 1935 and the wheels had gone a year later. The mill suffered bomb damage in the Second World War and only the wheel channels can now be seen. Sketch in Foreword

HORAM MILL (Horam TQ 583173)
A small corn mill with iron overshot wheel and shaft driving two pairs of stones by a lay shaft. The building had a brick substructure with a timber framed and weatherboarded superstructure with a gabled roof covered with clay tiles. The mill was complete in 1936, being used to generate electricity. By 1959 the machinery and wheel had been removed and the building was subsequently burnt out.
LITTLE BUCKINGHAM FARM MILL (Shoreham by Sea TQ 216062)
A small corn mill with rendered walls and a hipped roof covered with slates. It was converted into a house before 1937 and has since been demolished.
LOWDER MILL, Haslemere (Fernhurst SU 304317)
A medium sized corn mill with overshot wheel. The building is of stone with a half hipped roof covered with clay tiles. Gutted of its machinery, it was being used as a garden store in 1940.
OLIVER'S MILL, Haslemere (Linchmere SU 883325)
A medium sized corn mill on the River Wey with overshot wheel, replaced by a turbine. The building is of sandstone rubble with a gabled roof. The mill was in use in 1940. The internal machinery was removed in the 1950s and the mill has since been converted into a house.
REDGATE MILL (Rotherfield TQ 552324)
A small mill with overshot wheel. The building has a sandstone rubble substructure and timber framed and weatherboarded superstructure with half hipped roof covered with clay tiles. The machinery was removed long ago and the building was at one time used as a cattle shed. It has since been converted into a house with part of a modern waterwheel set alongside.
RUNCTON MILL (North Mundham SU 880022)
A medium sized corn mill on Pagham Rife with breast shot wheel. The building is of brick with a

hipped roof covered with clay tiles. Steam power was installed at an early date, with a separate boiler and engine house. It was converted to a house before the Second World War.

SHERIFF'S FARM MILL, Burstow Hill (Ardingly TQ 359288)

A corn mill with overshot composite wheel driving three pairs of stones. It had steam powe as well. The mill was demolished in 1931, leaving the wheel and some brickwork. There are now no remains on site.

SLINFOLD MILL (Slinfold TQ 124312)

A medium sized corn mill of brick construction with hipped roof covered with clay tiles. The mill remains were converted into a garage by 1936 and all the machinery was removed.

SOUTH HARTING MILL (Harting SU 790197)

A small corn mill of brick construction. Only some walls were standing in 1937.

STEDHAM MILL (Stedham with Iping SU 864231)

A medium sized corn mill on the Western River Rother, replaced early in the 20th century by a larger building housing a roller plant. When this burnt down a small building was erected housing a turbine and electric generator. This building is of stone rubble with a clay tiled hipped roof.

TABLEHURST MILL (Forest Row TQ 430352)

A corn mill with two overshot wheels in tandem. It ceased working in 1925 and was demolished by 1936.

TIDEBROOK MILL (Wadhurst TQ 609297)

A medium sized corn mill on Tide Brook. The building has a stone substructure and brick superstructure with a half hipped roof covered with clay tiles. It had been converted into a house well before 1937.

WANNOCK MILL (Willingdon TQ 574033)

A small corn mill on the Wannock Mill Stream with overshot wheel with wooden shaft. The building had a timber framed and weatherboarded superstructure and a gabled roof. The mill was derelict in 1936, although part of it was used as a tea room. It was demolished in the 1950s.

WARBLETON MILL (Warbleton TQ 621180)
A corn mill with overshot wheel and iron shaft. The only remains in 1936 were the wheel pit, shaft and penstock. It has a since been demolished.

WESTBOURNE MILL (Westbourne SU 757078)
A small corn mill on the River Ems with iron overshot wheel driving three pairs of stones through all iron machinery. The building is of brick. The mill was derelict in 1951 and was converted into a house in 1958 when all the woodwork of the wheel was removed.

The wheel of Westbourne Mill

WITHERENDEN MILL (Ticehurst TQ 653268)
A small corn mill with iron breast shot wheel and shaft. The building was of brick with a gabled roof replacing an earlier complex roof. The mill was operating to generate electricity and to power a saw bench between 1930 and the 1960s. It was demolished c 1970 and there are no remains.

GLOSSARY

ARMFIELD TURBINE A turbine made at the Ringwood works of millwright and founder Joseph J Armfield. The firm's two principal turbines were the River Patent and the British Empire, both of which were produced from the late 19th century onwards. The firm no longer exists.

BACKSHOT WHEEL See **PITCHBACK WHEEL**.

BOLTER A mechanical device for separating fLour from bran by beating it through a rotating cylinder of cloth. This was at first of wool, then calico and latterly of silk, hence the term 'silks'. Other cloths could also be used. The bolter was introduced in the 16th century.

BREAST SHOT WHEEL A waterwheel which is turned by the weight of water in its buckets, the water entering the buckets at about the level of the wheelshaft. It was developed in the 18th and 19th centuries. See also **LOW BREAST WHEEL**.

CLASP ARM WHEEL A wheel where two pairs of spokes form a square through which the shaft passes. Wedges are inserted to centre and ensure a tight fit. Increasingly used from the 18th century onwards. The design first appeared in Dutch mill books from 1728.

CROWN WHEEL A horizontal bevel gear wheel mounted above the great spur wheel near the top of the main upright shaft, from which secondary drives may be taken for auxiliary machinery, including sack hoist.

GAMBREL ROOF A roof of two different pitches, the lower one being steeper than the upper one. The roof may be either gabled or hipped.

GILKES TURBINE A turbine manufactured by a company at Kendal that still repairs and makes turbines. It has bought up many other turbine makers over the years and is now the principal turbine company in the UK.

GREAT SPUR WHEEL Main driving wheel mounted on the **UPRIGHT SHAFT** , transmitting drive to the stones via stone nuts. It may also provide drive for ancillary machinery.

HALF HIPPED ROOF A roof with a gabled end surmounted by a hipped roof.

HIPPED ROOF A ridged roof with two or more adjacent roof slopes. The hips may be covered with half round or angular ridge tiles, or with bonnet hip tiles.

HURST Heavy timber or iron framework supporting mill stones at about floor level and enclosing the main gearing in a watermill or windmill. Sometimes independent of the main structure of the mill, especially in the USA.

HURSTING See **HURST**.

LAYSHAFT See **LINE SHAFT**.

LINE SHAFT A horizontal driving shaft taking power from the prime mover to the driven machinery. Usually provided with belt pulleys to drive the machines, otherwise with gears. A horizontal shaft for transmitting power to additional equipment by belts or gears.

LOW BREAST WHEEL Waterwheel receiving water below axle height. Developed in the 18th and 19th centuries.

LUCAM A projecting gable or dormer enclosing the sack hoist on a watermill. Also known as Birdnest, Lucarne, Luccam, Lucombe and Lucomb. From the French, Lucarne.

MILLSTONES Peak - one piece stone made of millstone grit from the Peak District; Burr - usually built up stones of a hard chert imported from the Paris basin.

OVERSHOT WHEEL Where water is carried just beyond the top of the wheel, discharging into buckets on the far side, turning it in the same direction as the flow along the trough, utilising the weight of water to turn it.

PENSTOCK A sluice gate controlling the flow of water on to the wheel or launder, or the tube conveying water to a turbine.

PENTROUGH A tank, or channel of wood or metal, with a penstock, feeding water to an overshot, pitchback or high breast wheel.

PIT WHEEL The primary gearwheel mounted on the inner end of the wheel shaft, often in or partly in a pit in the mill floor.

PITCHBACK WHEEL A waterwheel where the water is delivered at the buckets at the top of the wheel on the same side as the launder. Usually the bottom of the wheel rotates in the same direction as the water in the tailrace.

PONCELET WHEEL An improved type of lightly constructed undershot waterwheel designed to run fast, fitted with metal floats curved to a specific pattern. The water is channelled below an inclined sluice. Invented by General JV Poncelet in 1824.

PUG MILL A machine for mixing and homogenising clay in preparation for shaping it into bricks.

QUOINS Stones or bricks forming the external angles of buildings, often accentuated with a different material or colour from that of the walls.

ROLLER MILLING A 19th century development (Budapest 1839, Britain 1880) in which the grain is gradually reduced to flour by being repeatedly passed between pairs of rollers. The rollers are set progressively closer together and sieving takes place between each pair, to separate flour from bran and germ. The rollers rotate with different surface speeds to facilitate the grinding process. Rollers which deal with whole grain and coarser particles are fluted to enable them to operate effectively. Some rollers may employ water cooling to limit the temperature rise of the product.

SLUICE A gate to control the flow of water, by raising or lower it. See **PENSTOCK**.

SPILLWAY A cill over which excess water spills.

SPUR WHEEL See **GREAT SPUR WHEEL** and **SPUR WHEEL GEAR.**

SPUR WHEEL GEAR Gear wheels in which the teeth project radially from the rim.

STONE NUT A pinion on a stone spindle which takes the drive from the spur wheel to the stones.

TURBINE See **WATER TURBINE**

UNDERSHOT WHEEL Used in lower courses, driven by a slight fall but larger volume of water.

UPRIGHT SHAFT The main vertical driving shaft of a watermill or windmill upon which the **WALLOWER**, the **GREAT SPUR WHEEL** and the **CROWN WHEEL** are mounted. Also called a main shaft.

WALLOWER The horizontal bevel gear or lantern pinion driven by the brake wheel or **PIT WHEEL** to turn the **UPRIGHT SHAFT** or **LAYSHAFT**, being the first driven gear wheel in wind- or watermill.

WATER TURBINE A 19th century development using an enclosed impeller whose cups or blades are scientifically shaped, driven by impulse and reaction of water. The casting commonly contains vanes or water flow control devices whereby the output power can be controlled. A higher efficiency and increased speeds and power are obtained compared with waterwheels.

WIRE MACHINE For sifting flour. Brushes revolve in a gauze lined cylinder to separate grades of flour.

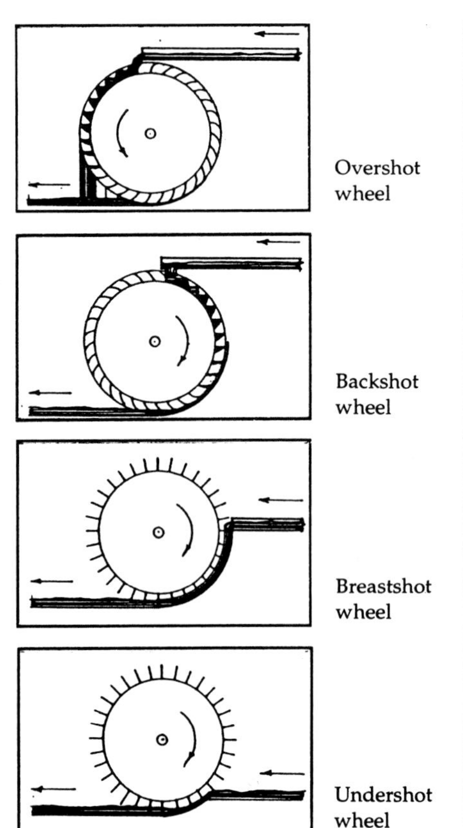
Overshot
wheel
Backshot
wheel
Breastshot
wheel
Undershot
wheel

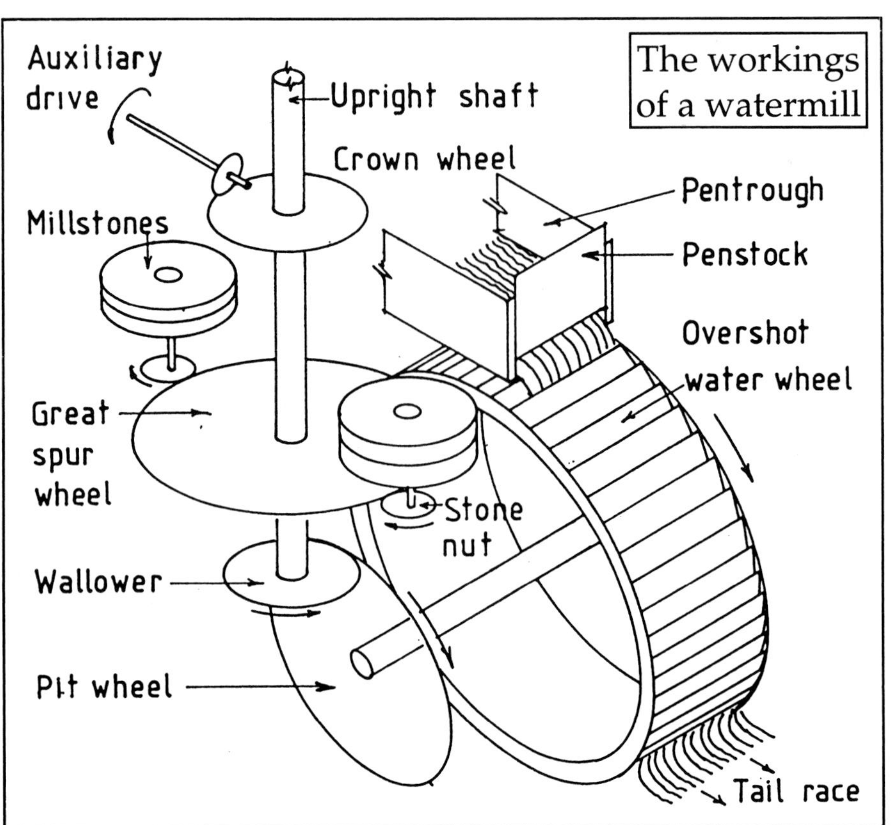
The workings
of a watermill
Auxiliary
drive
Upright shaft
Crown wheel
Pentrough
Millstones
Penstock
Overshot
water wheel
Great
spur
wheel
Stone
nut
Wallower
Pit wheel
Tail race

INDEX